Published in Great Britain in 2014 by Canongate Books Ltd,
14 High Street, Edinburgh EH1 1TE

www.canongate.tv

1

British Library Cataloguing-in-Publication Data
A catalogue record for this book is available on
request from the British Library

ISBN 978 1 78211 311 9
Paperback ISBN 978 1 78211 550 2

PEANUTS written and drawn by Charles M. Schulz
Edited by Andy Miller and Jenny Lord
Design: Rafaela Romaya
Layout: Stuart Polson

CHARLES M. SCHULZ

LIFE LESSONS FROM
LUCY

CANONGATE

Edinburgh · London

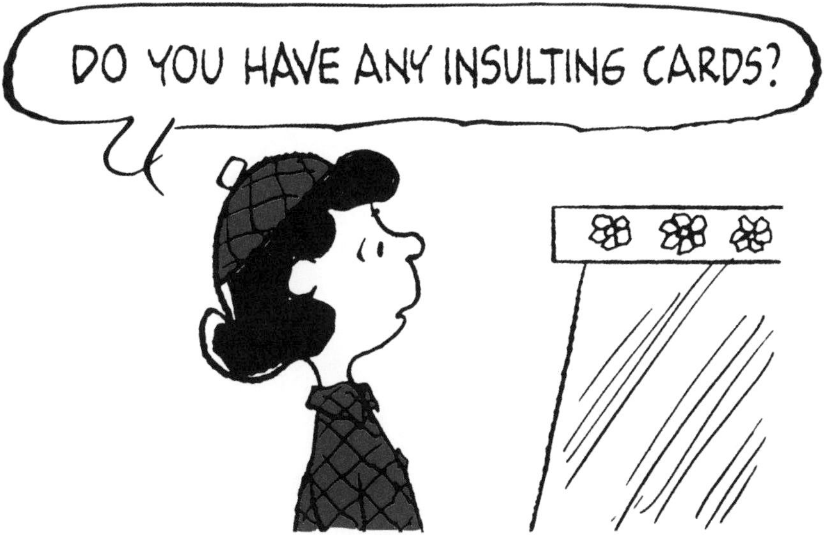
DO YOU HAVE ANY INSULTING CARDS?